A STAFFORD QUIZ BOOK

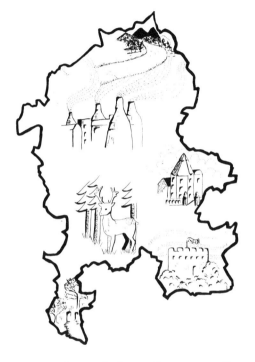

Testing your knowledge of town and country,
history and geography, yesterday and today

John Godwin

illustrated by Linda Prescott

S.B. Publications

By the same author:–

The Murder of Christina Collins
The Pocket Palmer
Beaudesert, The Pagets and Waterloo
Tom Coulthwaite, Wizard of the Turf †
Some Eighteenth Century Staffordshire MPs *
Early Aeronautics in Staffordshire *

The above books are obtainable from the author, except:–
† obtainable from the Valley Heritage Centre, Hednesford, Staffordshire;
* obtainable from Staffordshire County Library, Friars Terrace, Stafford.

First published in 1994 by S.B. Publications
c/o 19 Grove Road, Seaford, East Sussex BN25 1TP

ISBN 1 85770 069 4

Typeset, printed and bound by
Manchester Free Press, Longford Trading Estate,
Thomas Street, Stretford, Manchester M32 0JT

CONTENTS

Front Cover: Where is this folly?
Back Cover: Where is this village cross
　　　　　　　(Answers on page 63)

INTRODUCTION

In this booklet I have assumed the County of Staffordshire to be the area within its pre-1974 boundaries, and to include, therefore, a large slice of the Black Country, including Wolverhampton and Walsall. No county can claim a greater diversity of human activity than Staffordshire. The Moorlands of the north, the Potteries conurbation, the lush pastures of the Trent valley, the heathland of Cannock Chase, the varied industry of the Black Country, and the lovely countryside of the extreme south-west of Staffordshire combine to offer the traveller an unsurpassed variety of scenery and human toil. The questions in this booklet do, it is hoped, reflect this diversity.

I have tried to confine questions to those worth asking, and to those to which a positive and precise answer can be given. Not all the people mentioned were born in Staffordshire, but all are connected with its history.

I am most grateful to Mr. Derek Beard, formerly of Hanley Public Library; to Mr. Herman Dyson, formerly Western Divisional Librarian of Staffordshire; to Mr. Harry Taylor, the Editor of *The Bugle*; to Mr. Arthur Wood, formerly on the staff of Radio Stoke-on-Trent; and to Mr. Jack Moore of Nottingham, for their kind help in checking questions and in offering suggestions.

John Godwin
Rugeley, Staffs

Where is this mill? (answer on page 63)

THE QUIZ

1. THE ARTS

*Dead he is not,
but departed,
for the artist never dies.*

(Longfellow)

1. Which literary lady earned for herself the title "The Swan of Lichfield"?

2. Name Sir Francis Chantrey's most famous sculpture in Lichfield Cathedral.

3. Name the lady who created the sculpture of Captain Smith of the *Titanic* in Beacon Park, Lichfield.

4. Name the most famous artist and designer employed by Josiah Wedgwood in his pottery works.

5. "Sea Drift" by Delius was first performed in 1908 — where?

6. Name the Wolverhampton poet who wrote "The Highwayman".

7. Which Staffordshire composer wrote "The Gothic Symphony"?

8. One of England's most famous actors; always associated with Lichfield. Who was he?

9. Name Stone's famous water-colour landscape artist.

10. Where can one find the sculptured figure of a cat, on a plinth in a park? The figure is said to have been placed there in memory of a cat which went on a famous voyage round the world with its well-known owner.

2. BATTLES AND WARTIME

For what can war but endless war still breed?

(John Milton)

1. Name two well-known army camps on Cannock Chase in World War I.

2. A dump of between 3,000 and 4,000 tons of high-explosive bombs and ammunition exploded in Staffordshire during World War II. Where?

3. He marched through a Staffordshire town in 1745, on his way to Derby; returning four days later to plunder the town. Who?

4. Name the Civil War battle which took place near Stafford.

5. Name the son of an Archdeacon of Stafford who was closely involved in the Indian Mutiny, and who shot the Princes of Delhi.

6. Name the operational RAF station, near Alrewas, from which bombers set out to bomb Cologne in a thousand-bomber raid.

7. Name the man who was said to have sounded the trumpet for the 17th Lancers at the Charge of the Light Brigade, and who is buried with his trumpet in Lichfield.

8. Name the large arms factory in North Staffordshire which is said to have been named in broadcast threats by German propagandist "Lord Haw-Haw" (William Joyce) during World War II.

9. Name the famous Staffordshire cavalry man who was Second-in-Command to the Duke of Wellington at the Battle of Waterloo.

10. Lord Audley, commanding a Lancastrian army, was killed in one of the battles of the Wars of the Roses, fought in Staffordshire. Name the battle.

3. CANALS

The quiet waters by
(popular hymn)

1. Name the Derbyshire-born millwright who engineered the route of the Trent and Mersey Canal through Staffordshire.

2. Give the alternative name of the Trent and Mersey Canal, often used in earlier days.

3. Which Staffordshire canal originally terminated in Uttoxeter?

4. Name the parallel canal tunnels on the Trent and Mersey Canal on the Staffordshire-Cheshire border — one of which is now out of action and disused.

5. Which South Staffordshire town has been called "The Venice of the Midlands" because of its network of canals?

6. Name the lady murdered by boatmen on the Trent and Mersey Canal in the 1839 "Bloody Steps" murder — a story adapted by Colin Dexter in his Inspector Morse novel, "The Wench is Dead".

7. Name a lovely artificial lake in North Staffordshire, built to feed the canal system there.

8. Name the village where the Trent and Mersey Canal joins the Staffordshire and Worcestershire Canal.

9. Name the highest canal in Staffordshire.

10. Where does the Coventry Canal join the Trent and Mersey Canal?

4. CASTLES

This castle hath a pleasant seat
(Macbeth)

1. Name the Staffordshire castle containing fortifications built soon after the Norman Conquest, and associated with Robert de Marmion.

2. This castle stands close to the Stafford-to-Uttoxeter road, and belonged to the Ferrers family.

3. Name a mock castle ruin on the Staffordshire-Cheshire border.

4. Name the home of the Staffordshire man who became Archbishop of Canterbury in the reign of Mary Tudor.

5. Name a castle well known to Mary Queen of Scots when imprisoned in Staffordshire. She found it damp and evil-smelling.

6. A castle said to have been built by Bishop Walter Langton, Bishop of Lichfield. Where?

7. There are, in the Churnet Valley, the remains of a mediaeval castle — not to be confused with the nineteenth-century home of the Earls of Shrewsbury. Name the castle.

8. At the end of the nineteenth century this castle was purchased from Lord Townshend, and is now a museum. Name it.

9. Name the site of an Iron Age hill fort on Cannock Chase.

10. The present house — looking like a fortress — was built by Matthew Cradock, one of the founders of Massachusetts. Name it.

5. CHURCHES

A church is God between four walls
(Victor Hugo)

1. A Staffordshire church containing a memorial to Sir Garnet Wolseley, one-time Commander in Chief of the British Army, is also the burial place of Commodore George Anson, one-time First Lord of the Admiralty. Which church?

2. Name the designer of Cheadle's fine Roman Catholic church

3. Name the church which is supposed to be the only Wren Church in Staffordshire

4. The deeply recessed west doorway of this church in the east of Staffordshire contains one of the finest examples of Norman architecture in the county. Which church?

5. A famous nineteenth-century explorer came to Brereton to talk about his travels, and left, on a map, his markings to show the places he had visited. This map hangs in the church. Which explorer?

6. A beautiful church near Burton-on-Trent was built in the last century as a shrine to a dead husband. Which church?

7. A church in the county contains the tomb of St. Bertram, to which pilgrims came for cure or consolation. Which church?

8. Which church is said to be the first in England to be lit by electricity?

9. About the year 1866, a large organ was removed from Lichfield Cathedral to make room for an even larger one. To which church was the organ taken?

10. A small village church — half very old, half quite modern — containing ancient tombs, including that of a crusader. Which church?

6. COUNTRY MANSIONS

The stately homes of England,
How beautiful they stand
(Felicia Hemans)

1. Name the hall which was the seat of the Vernon family. The surrounding park gives its name to a service station on the M6.

2. A famous hall on Cannock Chase, demolished in the 1930s. Name it. It was the home of the Paget family.

3. Name the two former grounds, both of country houses, which later became amusement parks in the county.

4. Name a country house, near Wolverhampton, where Charles II hid from the Roundheads.

5. Name the residence of the Giffard family, one member of which was a double agent at the time Mary Queen of Scots was a prisoner of Elizabeth.

6. Name a hall which was formerly the home of the Sneyd family, but is now part of a University.

7. James Bateman planted an exotic garden at . . . ?

8. Name a country mansion pulled down many years ago, but which has an imposing Tudor gatehouse still standing.

9. Once a residence of the Worthington family (brewers); now a school for dyslexic children. Name it.

10. Once the seat of the Chetwynds and the Talbots, but purchased in 1960 by West Bromwich authority for use as an arts centre.

7. DIALECT

*Most of their discourse
was about hunting,
in a dialect I understood
very little.*
(Samuel Pepys)

1. What is meant by being "Clemm'd to jeth"? (South Staffordshire)

2. What is a "glarney"? (South Staffordshire)

3. What was a "bonkie"? (throughout Staffordshire)

4. What is "cag-mag"? (throughout Staffordshire)

5. What is "blarting"? (throughout Staffordshire)

6. What is an "asker"? (throughout Staffordshire)

7. What is a "ganzy"? (North Staffordshire)

8. What is a "doffer" (or "doffee")? (North Staffordshire)

9. What is a "chonnock"? (North Staffordshire)

10. What is "chelping"? (North Staffordshire)

8. FAMOUS MEN

Let us now praise famous men
(Apocrypha)

1. Name a world-famous potter who lost a leg.

2. Name a famous eighteenth-century doctor who practised in Lichfield, and who had an even-more-famous grandson.

3. Name a famous sailor, from near Stone, who became First Lord of the Admiralty.

4. Name a famous sailor, from Cannock Chase, who made a well-known journey around the world from 1740 to 1744.

5. Name the Staffordshire designer of the Spitfire.

6. Name a famous playwright who became MP for Stafford.

7. Name the founder of a London Hospital who was an MP for Tamworth.

8. Name the North Staffordshire miner who became Prime Minister of Australia.

9. Name the Manchester man who came to Cannock Chase, and trained three Grand National winners there.

10. Name a famous Lichfield Egyptologist who became His Britannic Majesty's Consul General in Egypt, and who sent back many ancient items to the British Museum.

9. FAMOUS WOMEN

Being a woman is a
terribly difficult trade,
since it consists principally
of dealing with men

(Joseph Conrad)

1. A famous nurse who gave her life to the town of Walsall in the nineteenth century. Who?

2. A famous North Staffordshire variety artiste, who made popular the song *There's an Old Mill by the Stream*, earlier this century. A street in the Potteries is named after her. Who is it?

3. A famous film star of the 1930s and 1940s, born in West Bromwich, who starred in *The Thirty Nine Steps* (1935) and *The Prisoner of Zenda* (1937). Who?

4. Name the well-known lady who set up the Roman Catholic convent at Stone in the in the nineteenth century.

5. A wall monument in Croxall Church mentions the lady from nearby Catton Hall, about whom the poet Byron wrote, "She walks in beauty, like the night." Name the lady.

6. The famous wife of Earl Leofric, who had one of his country estates at King's Bromley. Who was she?

7. A famous Warwickshire writer who had close connections with Ella one, Staffordshire, and who wrote about it (under another na' e) in one of her books. Who?

8. .er father was Vicar of Shareshill, near Cannock. She wrote the well-known hymn, *Take My Life and Let it Be,* and many others. Who was she?

9. She lived in Uttoxeter in the .nineteenth century, and wrote or edited about a hundred books. Who was she?

10. A woman commemorated by a wall plaque in Lichfield cathedral achieved fame because she first introduced inoculation against smallpox into this country. Who was she?

10. GEOGRAPHY AND HISTORY

There is history in all men's lives
(William Shakespeare — *Henry IV*)

1. When this country was divided into several kingdoms, Staffordshire was part of which?

2. A famous air race of 1910 (won by a Frenchman) went right across Staffordshire — from Tamworth to Madeley. Name the race.

3. Until 1890, the county boundary ran through the middle of one Staffordshire town. Which?

4. Charles Dickens said of this town, in 1862, "As dull and dead a town as anyone could desire not to see." Which town?

5. The river forming the north-eastern boundary of Staffordshire is . . . ?

6. Which river forms the boundary of Staffordshire for a short distance in the extreme north, on the Cheshire side?

7. Name the town which, in the eighteenth and part of the nineteenth century, was perhaps more notorious than any other for bribery and corruption at election times, and which was in fact nearly disenfranchised.

8. A man who lived at Chetwynd House, Stafford (now the Post Office), and who is regarded as the pioneer of the Stafford boot and shoe industry. Who is this?

9. A saltworks until 1901, taking its name from the family name of Lord Ferrers, was to be found at . . . ?

10. Charles II was refused Holy Communion, because of his immoral life, by a Staffordshire Archbishop of Canterbury. Who was this?

11. GOD'S CREATURES

Nature knows a thing or two

(Sir Owen Seaman)

1. A special breed of shaggy-haired cattle roamed a Staffordshire estate in bygone days. Which estate was this?

2. Name the place where the multi-coloured Russell lupins were first grown.

3. An animal associated with Chillington Hall, and with the words "Prenez haleine, tirez fort". Name the animal.

4. Which Staffordshire factory made a model of a whale for use in the film *Moby Dick*?

5. Limestone trackways in North Staffordshire are named as one of the rare habitats of *lampyris noctiluca*. Give the common name for this creature.

6. Along some waterways of Staffordshire, one can see the sapphire flash of *alcedo atthis*. Give the name in general use for this creature.

7. A large reservoir crossed by a long causeway in mid-Staffordshire is now a well-established attraction for the ornithologists. Which reservoir?

8. A species of animal with antipodean connections has escaped into the wilds of the Staffordshire Moorlands, Name the creature.

9. Which of the Potteries towns was associated with bear-baiting, as described by Arnold Bennett in *The Elixir of Youth*? (The sport was banned in 1837.)

10. Name a breed of Staffordshire pig with golden hair and pink skin.

12. INDUSTRY

*Every man's work shall
be made manifest*
(Corinthians 1 – 3·13)

1. Which Black Country town became famous for its locks and keys?

2. Where are JCB diggers made?

3. Name one of the two Staffordshire towns famous for crystal ware.

4. Name the potter who adopted the willow pattern on his pottery.

5. Name the lorry-building firm which was associated with Wolverhampton.

6. Who built the first of his Black Country furnaces near Bilston, and became known as "The Father of the South Staffordshire iron trade"?

7. Name a town famous for silk manufacture, introduced by the Huguenots in the seventeenth century.

8. Name the town, then in Staffordshire, which produced the main anchor chain and the anchors for the liner *Queen Mary*.

9. Name a famous pickle which took its name from the Staffordshire village where the factory used to be located.

10. Where, in the eighteenth century, was the largest and deepest (1,200 feet) copper mine in Britain?

13. INVENTIONS, DISCOVERIES AND ACHIEVEMENTS

Some achieve greatness, and some have greatness thrust upon them

(William Shakespeare — *Twelfth Night*)

1. A famous North Staffordshire scientist, who was an early pioneer of radio, also experimented in spiritualism. Name him.

2. Which Staffordshire sailor has been called "The Father of the Navy", and is also said to have started the Marines?

3. His great invention was a machine which could accurately bore the barrel of a gun. Who was he?

4. Although an eighteenth-century doctor of medicine, he designed a speaking machine, a steam turbine, telescopes, pumps and even forecast "flying chariots". Who was he?

5. He is often described as "The Father of Photography", because of his early photographic experiments. Who was he?

6. He conducted scientific experiments into the use of the drug digitalis (obtained from the foxglove) for certain medical conditions. He married a Stafford lady, and took charge of the hospital there for a time. Who was he?

7. Boulton and Watt's steam engines were made in a manufactory in a part of Birmingham which was then part of Staffordshire. Name the area.

8. A cotton mill, alongside the River Dove, was built in 1782 at Rocester by the inventor of the spinning frame. Who was this?

9. A man who, according to his church memorial, built "the unequalled arch of the Grosvenor Bridge over the River Dee in Chester", and who died in 1853. Who was he?

10. In 1822, the first iron steamship, the Aaron Manby, was made at . . . ?

14. MISCELLANEOUS

*Memory is the diary that
we all carry about with us*
(Oscar Wilde)

1. Name the world-famous geologist who was President of the British Association in 1910, and who was born in Rugeley.

2. Name a well-known Staffordshire poet who wrote *Drake's Drum* and *Vitaï Lampada.*

3. Sir Arthur Conan Doyle, creator of Sherlock Holmes, came to Staffordshire to help solve a crime. Which crime, and where?

4. Early in the nineteenth century, a lady in Staffordshire created a sensation by insisting that she had not had anything to eat for five years, or to drink for four. Name her.

5. Name the highest point in Staffordshire.

6. Name the four counties which are said to meet at a point marked by a cross on the cellar ceiling of the Four Counties Public House at No Man's Heath, near Clifton Campville.

7. In the 1860s, the world-record altitude in a balloon was achieved by two men ascending from Wolverhampton. Name the men.

8. Which doctor, from Hints near Lichfield, earned himself the title of "The Father of Geriatrics" for his special study of the needs of old men?

9. Where does the River Trent rise?

10. Name the Staffordshire village where the core of the first Atlantic cable was made.

15. CURIOSITIES

The curious here,
to feed a craving mind
(Crabbe)

1. Name the house, then in Staffordshire, to which the Gunpowder Plotters fled.

2. The mother of a famous Prime Minister was the sister of a lady whose son took his name from a North Staffordshire beauty spot. Name the Prime Minister.

3. Name the area in north Staffordshire where hills of stark millstone grit point to the sky.

4. The Glyn Arms at Himley is better known as . . . ?

5. Name a man who raised many hundreds of pounds for charity by impersonating a famous Scottish entertainer. He came from Hixon.

6. Colonel William Carlos, who supported the head of Charles II while he slept in the oak tree at Boscobel, is buried where?

7. During the Civil War, Lord Brooke — one of the Roundhead military leaders — was shot and killed by a man taking aim from the Cathedral, Name the man.

8. One of the county's most ancient dances takes place in September. Name the village where the dance takes place.

9. A 104-acre bog, being a raft of peat on water up to fifteen metres deep, is highly dangerous. Where is it?

10. Name the Staffordshire town from which the 'double sunset' phenomenon can be seen on certain summer days.

16. RAILWAYS

My private joy,
both man and boy,
is being a railroad rider
(Ogden Nash)

1. Name the railway, opened in 1847, joining Rugby and Stafford directly, rather than through Birmingham and Wolverhampton.

2. A railway line joining Walsall to Cannock was extended to Rugeley. Give the original name of this latter section.

3. A central-Staffordshire landowner refused to let the main line pass across his land, except through a tunnel, which is only a few feet below the surface of the land. Where is this?

4. Name the narrow-gauge railway which lasted only about thirty years, and which went from Waterhouses to Hulme End in north-east Staffordshire.

5. A Staffordshire Earl insisted on a request stop for London expresses passing through his small station. Name the Earl.

6. By what name was the North Staffordshire Railway popularly known?

7. In what year was the railway station which replaced the earlier 1862 one built at Stafford?

8. The railway joining Birmingham to Merseyside, which opened in 1837, was named . . . ?

9. Which two railway companies fought for the Black Country traffic in the 1850s, resulting in two railway systems between Birmingham and Wolverhampton?

10. Name any two main-line stations which have been closed between Stafford and Lichfield.

17. RELIGION

A good man was ther of religioun
(Chaucer)

1. Name the denomination of the Christian religion started by Hugh Bourne in North Staffordshire in the nineteenth century.

2. Name the man from Stourton Castle who twice nearly became Pope.

3. Name the man born in the Rectory at Whitmore who wrote the hymn *The Church's One Foundation*.

4. Name the leader of a religious denomination who walked through Lichfield crying, "Woe unto the bloody City of Lichfield."

5. The last heretic in England to die at the stake was burned in Lichfield. Who was this?

6. In which town did the mob threaten to "knock the brains out" of John Wesley, when he preached there?

7. Name the small Staffordshire town where the Bishops of Lichfield used to live, and where six Bishops are said to be buried.

8. The son of a man who lived for some time in the Close in Lichfield, translated into English, the words of *Adeste Fideles* (*O Come all ye Faithful*). Who was this?

9. Name the man who was Vicar of Cannock about the year 1700, and whose sermons were burned by the common hangman after he preached against the "Glorious Revolution".

10. Name a famous Bishop of Lichfield who had earlier been the one and only Bishop of New Zealand.

18. ROGUES, CRIMINALS AND ECCENTRICS

Crimes, like virtues,
are their own reward

(George Farquhar)

1. Name the world-famous eccentric philosopher who wrote books on education and philosophy, and who stayed at Wootton Hall, near Ellastone, for a year to avoid persecution on mainland Europe.

2. Name a Cannock doctor, an eccentric, who kept a large menagerie behind his house.

3. Name the eighteenth-century hermit of Cannock Chase.

4. Name Wolverhampton's most notorious rogue.

5. Name a moorland village, in the far north of the county, which was said to be the home of counterfeiters.

6. Name the doctor who practised in the Potteries, and who in 1797, shot and killed the father of the lady he would like to have married.

7. The notorious nineteenth-century poisoner of Rugeley was . . . ?

8. Lord Aston (from Tixall Hall) and Lord Stafford were falsely accused of sinister plottings at the time of the so-called Popish Plot, by a steward of Lord Aston, a man of doubtful character. Name him.

9. Name the leader of the Gunpowder Plotters who fled with others to Kingswinford after Guy Fawkes was discovered in the Houses of Parliament.

10. Name the double-agent who acted both for Mary Queen of Scots and for Queen Elizabeth's ministers in this country while Mary was a prisoner in Chartley Manor.

19. ROYALTY

*Royalty will be strong because
it appeals to diffused feelings*
(Walter Bagshot)

1. In spite of expressed doubt, folklore states that as Mary Queen of Scots went to Fotheringhay to face trial and execution, she spent the night at the Staffordshire village of . . . where?

2. In the early 1930s, a famous royal personality used to visit the well-known horse-racing stables run by Tom Coulthwaite on Cannock Chase. Who was this?

3. A King of England sold the old Cank Forest to raise money for the Third Crusade. Which King was this?

4. Which King granted Stafford's first surviving charter?

5. Which royal person opened Blithfield Reservoir on 27th October, 1953?

6. Which royal person led the assault on Lichfield Cathedral and breached the defences of the Parliamentary forces in 1643?

7. Which member of the Royal Family was killed in an air crash at Halfpenny Green, South Staffordshire?

8. Where did Charles II meet Jane Lane, who helped him to escape to France after he disguised himself as her servant?

9. Where did Princess Marina and the Duke of Kent stay for their honeymoon in 1934?

10. A servant of Henry VIII for a quarter of a century, this man provided money to build the Church at Barton-under-Needwood, and was with Henry VIII at the Field of the Cloth of Gold. What was his name?

20. SPORT

The game, he said, *is never lost till won*
(Crabbe)

1. Which Staffordshire football team has won the F.A. Cup five times?

2. Which Staffordshire man bred the very first Derby winner?

3. Which football club, the second oldest in the country, provided the first Secretary of the Football League?

4. William Perry, a Black Country boxer of the nineteenth century, was popularly known as . . . ?

5. The results page in the Official Tug of War Handbook lists teams from a Staffordshire village as winning the World Outdoor Championships (at different weights) five times; the World Indoor Championships twice; the European Championships (at different weights) four times; and the World Games once. Which village?

6. Name the Hednesford boxer (an ex-miner) of the early 1920s who once went fifteen rounds with Len Harvey.

7. A Staffordshire football club is said to be the only one in the country to have provided goalkeeper and both full-backs in an international match. The players were Rowley, Clare and Underwood — can you name the team from which they came?

8. Name the Staffordshire cricketer who took the most wickets in the 1913–14 test series.

9. Which Staffordshire football teams (within the former county area) are known as: (a) the Potters; (b) The Baggies; (c) The Saddlers?

10. Name the former captain of the England Women's Cricket Team who comes from Wolverhampton.

21. TOWNS

God made the country,
and man made the towns
(Cowper)

1. Which town was sometimes referred to as 'Little Rome' because of the number of Roman Catholics living there?

2. Which Staffordshire town was once the capital of Mercia, and minted its own coins?

3. In what year did the six Pottery towns federate under the name of Stoke-on-Trent?

4. It was often called 'The Metropolis of the Moorlands', but is now more frequently known as 'The Queen of the Moorlands'. Name the town.

5. A town in close proximity to the Potteries , and much older than the pottery towns, and not a part of the federation. Name it.

6. A town which boasts of its 'Ancient High House', which now houses a museum. Which?

7. A town which has, in the Roman Catholic church, the tomb of Bishop Ullathorne of Birmingham; a man who, earlier in his life, exposed the horrors of the convict system in Australia, and helped to end the transportation there. Which town?

8. Name the town where St. Modwen is said to have founded an early Christian settlement.

9. In what town do we find the bronze bust of Seaman Carless, who won the Victoria Cross in a naval engagement in World War I, while serving as a gunner?

10. William Wood obtained a patent for issuing coins to the North American colonies in 1722. Where did he come from?

22. VILLAGES

*Among the pleasant
villages and farms*
(Milton)

1. Name the Staffordshire village which is the only one in Britain said to begin with a silent 'G'.

2. A North Staffordshire village claims to be the highest in England. Which?

3. Name the Staffordshire village once exempted from paying rates by royal decree.

4. The family home of the Mosley family — a member of which was Sir Oswald Mosley, the one-time leader of the British Union of Fascists – was in which village?

5. A Staffordshire hamlet was the birthplace of an Archbishop of Canterbury. Name the hamlet.

6. The burial place of a famous nineteenth-century Prime Minister can be found at the village of Drayton Bassett. Name the Prime Minister.

7. A Staffordshire village has a narrow bridge which crosses the Trent; the bridge has recesses over the buttresses so that the humble folk could seek refuge as the nobility came riding by. Name both the village and the bridge.

8. Will Willett claimed to have danced non-stop for twelve days and nights. The dance began on 2nd September, 1752, and ended on 14th September; but England dropped eleven days from the calendar at this time, so it lasted only a few hours. Where did the dance take place?

9. The grounds of a hall near a Staffordshire village inspired Dr. Johnson to write his book *Rasselas*, in which the lovely nearby valley is transported to Abyssinia. Name the village.

10. Thomas Gisborne, who lived at the now-demolished Yoxall Lodge, was visited from time to time in the late-eighteenth century by a man whose name became synonymous with the anti-slavery campaign of that time. This man was a national figure — name him.

23. WRITERS

Look in thy heart,
and write
(Sir Philip Sydney)

1. Name the most famous writer from the Potteries.

2. Name the famous Walsall-born writer who wrote *Three Men in a Boat*.

3. Who wrote *The Beaux' Stratagem* (1707), set in Lichfield? This was the playwright's last and best play, and it gave us the term 'Lady Bountiful'.

4. Name the famous writer born in India to parents who courted in North Staffordshire.

5. Which Staffordshire man wrote a famous book on fishing?

6. A famous lexicographer once kept a small school at Edial Hall. Who?

7. Who was known as 'The Moorland poet'?

8. Which female writer wrote *John Halifax, Gentleman*?

9. He wrote extensively on mental illness and its cure, he also wrote a book of verse; and is buried in Stone. Who is this?

10. A Staffordshire village churchyard contains the grave of the daughter of Thomas Moore, the poet, who wrote here his oriental romance *Lalla Rookh*. Name the village.

STAFFORDSHIRE PICTURE QUIZ

1. A great cleft in the rock on the Staffordshire-Cheshire border, where, according to tradition, the Lollards used to hold services. Where?

2. Once a magnificent garden; now something completely different. Where?

3. Once a stately home, now a health spa. Name it.

4. Name this village, from the church tower of which a Queen watched one of the battles of the War of the Roses.

5. Maimed horses: two of a series of maimings which occurred in a Staffordshire village around the turn of the century. Name the village.

6. Name this hall, now an arts centre.

7. A famous Chantrey sculpture. Name it.

8. Where is this?

9. Many thought him a miser, but he proved to be a great public benefactor — he built Tamworth Town Hall. Name him.

10. Used as a canal reservoir, its original name was Norton Pool. What is its present name?

11. A well-known Staffordshire Abbey ruins. Where?

12. A recent picture of a huge crater, the scene of England's biggest explosion. Where?

13. This seaplane, designed by a famous Staffordshire aircraft designer, won a celebrated international race in 1931. Name the race.

14. A small church of England building, erected by Thomas Gilbert, a well-known entrepreneur of the eighteenth century. Where is the building?

15. A famous Staffordshire man's statue in St. Paul's Cathedral. Whose?

16. The ruins of a famous hall on Cannock Chase, demolished in the 1930s. Which hall?

17. Two men set an altitude record in a balloon from Wolverhampton in the nineteenth century. Name them.

18. A fountain (now demolished) in Stafford was named after a famous son of the town who became Lord Mayor of London. Name him.

19. A narrow-gauge railway ran through the Manifold Valley earlier this century. Name the cave which can be seen on this picture

20. The son of a famous potter was a pioneer of photography, Name him.

21. One of Staffordshire's most infamous characters, who lived in
Rugeley in the last century, was publicly hanged. Who was this?

22. The winner of the 1931 Grand National was trained on Cannock Chase, Name the horse.

23. This shows one of the competitors in a famous 1910 cross-country air race, the route of which went right across Staffordshire. Name the race.

24. A famous Cannock doctor (left) kept a large private menagerie before World War I, and was advisor to the local circuses on their animals. Name the doctor.

25. The memorial in Lichfield Cathedral to a famous Bishop. He gave his
name to a college at Cambridge University. Which Bishop?

ANSWERS

1. THE ARTS

1. Anna Seward.

2. The Sleeping Children.

3. Lady Kathleen Scott, widow of Scott of the Antarctic.

4. John Flaxman.

5. Victoria Hall, Hanley.

6. Alfred Noyes.

7. Havergal Brian.

8. David Garrick.

9. Peter de Wint.

10. Shugborough Park.

2. BATTLES AND WARTIME

1. Rugeley (or Penkridge Bank) Camp and Brocton Camp.

2. Fauld, near Hanbury.

3. Bonnie Prince Charlie, the Young Pretender.

4. Hopton Heath

5. William Hodson of Hodson's Horse.

6. Fradley (but allow Lichfield).

7. John Brown.

8. Swynnerton.

9. William Henry Paget, Earl of Uxbridge — later the first Marquess of Anglesey.

10. Blore Heath.

3. CANALS

1. James Brindley.
2. The Grand Trunk.
3. The Caldon Canal.
4. Harecastle Tunnels.
5. Tipton.
6. Christina Collins.
7. Rudyard Lake.
8. Great Haywood.
9. Caldon Canal.
10. Fradley Junction.

4. CASTLES

1. Tamworth.
2. Chartley.
3. Mow Cop.
4. Stourton Castle.
5. Tutbury.
6. Eccleshall.
7. Alton Castle.
8. Tamworth.
9. Castle Ring.
10. Caverswall.

5. CHURCHES

1. Colwich.

2. A.W.N. Pugin.

3. Ingestre.

4. Tutbury.

5. David Livingstone.

6. Hoar Cross.

7. Ilam.

8. Chasetown.

9. Armitage.

10. Mavesyn Ridware.

6. COUNTRY MANSIONS

1. Hilton Hall — Hilton Park Services.

2. Beaudesert Hall.

3. Alton Towers; Drayton Manor.

4. Moseley Old Hall.

5. Chillington Hall.

6. Keele Hall.

7. Biddulph Grange.

8. Tixall Hall.

9. Maple Hayes.

10. Ingestre Hall.

7. DIALECT

1. "Starved to death."
2. A marble for playing.
3. A man who worked on the pit bank.
4. Inferior meat.
5. Crying loudly, like a baby.
6. A newt.
7. A woollen pullover.
8. A challenge.
9. A turnip.
10. Incessant chatter.

8. FAMOUS MEN

1. Josiah Wedgwood.
2. Erasmus Darwin.
3. John Jervis.
4. Lord George Anson.
5. Reginald Mitchell.
6. Richard Brinsley Sheridan.
7. Thomas Guy.
8. Joseph Cooke (he later dropped the 'e' from his surname).
9. Tom Coulthwaite.
10. Henry Salt.

9. FAMOUS WOMEN

1. Sister Dora Pattison.

2. Gertie Gitana.

3. Madeleine Carroll.

4. Mother Margaret Hallahan.

5. Lady Wilmot-Horton of Catton Hall.

6. Lady Godiva.

7. George Eliot (Mary Ann Evans).

8. Frances Ridley Havergal.

9. Mary Howitt.

10. Lady Mary Wortley Montague.

10. GEOGRAPHY AND HISTORY

1. Mercia.

2. The London-to-Manchester Air Race.

3. Tamworth.

4. Stafford.

5. The Dove.

6. The Dane.

7. Stafford.

8. William Horton (1750–1832).

9. Shirleywich.

10. Gilbert Sheldon (from Stanton, near Ellastone).

11. GOD'S CREATURES

1. Chartley.
2. Bakers of Codsall.
3. Panther (allow leopard).
4. Dunlop Special Products in the Potteries.
5. Glow-worm.
6. Kingfisher.
7. Blithfield.
8. Wallaby.
9. Burslem.
10. The Tamworth Pig.

12. INDUSTRY

1. Willenhall.
2. Rocester.
3. Tutbury or Brierley Hill.
4. Josiah Spode.
5. Guy Motors.
6. John "Iron Mad" Wilkinson.
7. Leek.
8. Brierley Hill — made by Samuel Taylor and Sons, Brettell Lane.
9. Branston Pickle.
10. Ecton, north-east Staffordshire.

13. INVENTIONS, DISCOVERIES AND ACHIEVEMENTS

1. Sir Oliver Lodge.

2. Lord Anson.

3. John "Iron Mad" Wilkinson.

4. Dr. Erasmus Darwin.

5. Thomas Wedgwood, son of Josiah.

6. Dr. Wiliam Withering.

7. Allow either Soho or Handsworth.

8. Richard Arkwright.

9. James Trubshaw — memorial in Colwich Church.

10. Tipton.

14. MISCELLANEOUS

1. Thomas Geoge Bonney.

2. Sir Henry Newbolt (born in Bilston).

3. The crimes of the so-called Wyrley Gang, near Walsall — horse-maiming outrages

4. Ann Moor of Tutbury.

5. Oliver Hill, Axe Edge, 1684 feet above sea level.

6. Staffordshire, Derbyshire, Leicestershire, Warwickshire.

7. Coxwell and Glaisher — they claim to have ascended seven miles.

8. Sir John Floyer.

9. Biddulph Moor.

10. Oakamoor.

15. CURIOSITIES

1. Holbeach House.

2. Stanley Baldwin (cousin to Rudyard Kipling).

3. The Roaches.

4. The Crooked House.

5. Wilmot Martin, "The Staffordshire Harry Lauder".

6. Brewood Churchyard.

7. Dumb Dyott.

8. Abbots Bromley.

9. Chartley Moss.

10. Leek.

16. RAILWAYS

1. Trent Valley Railway.

2. Cannock Mineral Line.

3. Shugborough Park.

4. Leek and Manifold Light Railway.

5. Earl of Harrowby: Sandon Station.

6. 'The Knotty'.

7. 1962.

8. Grand Junction Railway.

9. L.N.W.R. and G.W.R.

10. Milford; Colwich; Armitage — any two.

17. RELIGION

1. Primitive Methodism.
2. Cardinal Pole.
3. Samuel Stone.
4. George Fox, the Quaker.
5. Edward Wightman.
6. Wednesbury.
7. Eccleshall.
8. Rev. F. Oakeley.
9. Rev. Henry Sacheverell.
10. Bishop Selwyn.

18. ROGUES, CRIMINALS AND ECCENTRICS

1. Jean Jacques Rousseau.
2. Dr. J.K. Butter.
3. Dick Slee.
4. Jonathan Wild.
5. Flash.
6. Dr. Thomas Oliver.
7. Dr. William Palmer
8. Stephen Dugdale.
9. Robert Catesby.
10. Gilbert Giffard.

19. ROYALTY

1. Abbots Bromley.

2. Edward Prince of Wales.

3. Richard the Lion Heart.

4. King John.

5. Queen Elizabeth the Queen Mother.

6. Prince Rupert — grandson of James I.

7. H.R.H. Prince William of Gloucester.

8. Bentley Hall, near Walsall.

9. Himley Hall.

10. John Taylor.

20. SPORT

1. West Bromwich Albion.

2. Dick Vernon of Hilton Hall, near Cannock. The horse was Diomed

3. Stoke Football Club

4. The Tipton Slasher.

5. Sheen.

6. Albert Dando.

7. Stoke Football Club.

8. Sydney Barnes.

9. (a) Stoke City; (b) West Bromwich Albion; (c) Walsall.

10. Rachel Heyhoe-Flint.

21. TOWNS

1. Wolverhampton.
2. Tamworth.
3. 1910.
4. Leek.
5. Newcastle-under-Lyme.
6. Stafford.
7. Stone.
8. Burton-on-Trent.
9. Walsall.
10. Wolverhampton.

22. VILLAGES

1. Gnosall.
2. Flash.
3. Knighton.
4. Rolleston-on-Dove.
5. Stanton, near Ellastone. Gilbert Sheldon
6. Sir Robert Peel.
7. Great Haywood; Essex Bridge.
8. Endon.
9. Ilam.
10. William Wilberforce.

23. WRITERS

1. Arnold Bennett.

2. Jerome K. Jerome.

3. George Farquhar.

4. Rudyard Kipling.

5. Isaac Walton.

6. Samuel Johnson.

7. George Heath; died at 25, burried Horton churchyard.

8. Dinah Mulock, later Mrs. Craik.

9. Thomas Bakewell.

10. Mayfield.

24. PICTURE QUIZ

1. Ludchurch.

2. Alton Towers.

3. Hoar Cross Hall.

4. Mucklestone.

5. Great Wyrley.

6. Ingestre Hall.

7. The Sleeping Children.

8. Blithfield Hall.

9. Thomas Guy.

10. Chasewater.

11. Croxden Abbey.

12. Fauld, near Hanbury.

13. The Schneider Trophy Race.

14. Cotton.

15. Dr. Samuel Johnson

16. Beaudesert Hall.

17. Henry Coxwell and James Glaisher.

18. Thomas Sydney.

19. Thor's Cave.

20. Tom Wedgwood.

21. William Palmer.

22. Grakle.

23. The London-to-Manchester Air Race.

24. Dr. John Kerr Butter.

25. Bishop Selwyn.

S.B. Publications publish a wide range of local-history
titles on Staffordshire and around the country.
For full details write (enclosing S.A.E.) to:–
S.B. Publications
c/o 19 Grove Road,
Seaford,
East Sussex BN25 1TP.

Answers
Front Cover: The Ruin, Shugborough.
Back Cover: The Village Cross, Ilam.
Page 6: The Flint Mill, Cheddleton.